This Journal belongs to:

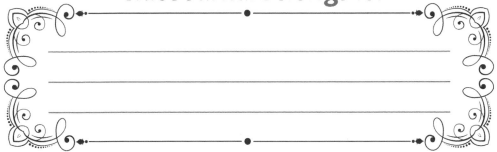

"The 32nd president of the United States"

"There is nothing so American as our national parks.... The fundamental idea behind the parks...is that the country belongs to the people, that it is in process of making for the enrichment of the lives of all of us."

-Franklin D. Roosevelt

	Name	Location	Date Est	Visiting Date
1	Acadia	Maine	Feb, 1919	
2	American Samoa	American Samoa	Oct, 1988	
3	Arches	Utah	Nov, 1971	
4	Badlands	South Dakota	Nov, 1978	
5	Big Bend	Texas	Feb, 1944	
6	Biscayne	Florida	Jun, 1980	
7	Black Canyon of the Gunnison	Colorado	Oct, 1999	
8	Bryce Canyon	Utah	Feb, 1928	
9	Canyonlands	Utah	Sep, 1964	
10	Capitol Reef	Utah	Dec, 1971	
11	Carlsbad Caverns	New Mexico	May, 1930	
12	Channel Islands	California	Mar, 1980	
13	Congaree	South Carolina	Nov, 2003	
14	Crater Lake	Oregon	May, 1902	
15	Cuyahoga Valley	Ohio	Oct, 2000	
16	Death Valley	California, Nevada	Oct, 1994	
17	Denali	Alaska	Feb, 1917	
18	Dry Tortugas	Florida	Oct, 1992	
19	Everglades	Florida	May, 1934	
20	Gates of the Arctic	Alaska	Dec, 1980	
21	Gateway Arch	Missouri	Feb, 2018	

	Name	Location	Date Est	Visiting Date
22	Glacier	Montana	May, 1910	
23	Glacier Bay	Alaska	Dec, 1980	
24	Grand Canyon	Arizona	Feb, 1919	
25	Grand Teton	Wyoming	Feb, 1929	
26	Great Basin	Nevada	Oct, 1986	
27	Great Sand Dunes	Colorado	Sep, 2004	
28	Great Smoky Mountains	North Carolina, Tennessee	Jun, 1934	
29	Guadalupe Mountains	Texas	Oct, 1966	
30	Haleakalā	Hawaii	Jul, 1961	
31	Hawai'i Volcanoes	Hawaii	Aug, 1916	
32	Hot Springs	Arkansas	Mar, 1921	
33	Indiana Dunes	Indiana	Feb, 2019	
34	Isle Royale	Michigan	Apr, 1940	
35	Joshua Tree	California	Oct, 1994	
36	Katmai	Alaska	Dec, 1980	
37	Kenai Fjords	Alaska	Dec, 1980	
38	Kings Canyon	California	Mar, 1940	
39	Dry Tortugas	Florida	Oct, 1992	
40	Kobuk Valley	Alaska	Dec, 1980	
41	Lake Clark	Alaska	Dec, 1980	
42	Lassen Volcanic	California	Aug, 1916	

	Name	Location	Date Est	Visiting Date
43	Mammoth Cave	Kentucky	Jul, 1941	
44	Mesa Verde	Colorado	Jun, 1906	
45	Mount Rainier	Washington	Mar, 1899	
46	New River Gorge	West Virginia	Dec, 2020	
47	North Cascades	Washington	Oct, 1968	
48	Olympic	Washington	Jun, 1938	
49	Petrified Forest	Arizona	Dec, 1962	
50	Pinnacles	California	Jan, 2013	
51	Redwood	California	Oct, 1968	
52	Rocky Mountain	Colorado	Jun, 1915	
53	Saguaro	Arizona	Oct, 1994	
54	Sequoia	California	Sep, 1890	
55	Shenandoah	Virginia	Dec, 1935	
56	Theodore Roosevelt	North Dakota	Nov, 1978	
57	Virgin Islands	U.S. Virgin Islands	Aug, 1956	
58	Voyageurs	Minnesota	Apr, 1975	
59	White Sands	New Mexico	Dec, 2019	
60	Wind Cave	South Dakota	Jan, 1903	
61	Wrangell–St. Elias	Alaska	Dec, 1980	
62	Yosemite	California	Oct, 1890	
63	Zion	Utah	Nov, 1919	

ACADIA

City/State Entered	Temp

  Wheather

Who Was With Me	Where We Stayed	Activities We Did

Wildlife

Sights

Impressions

My Favorite Memory

Places I Visited On The Park

Next Time I will

Notes

Will Return once again?

Yep / Nope

Overall Experience

AMERICAN SAMOA

City/State Entered	Temp

   Wheather

Who Was With Me	Where We Stayed	Activities We Did

Wildlife	Sights

Impressions

My Favorite Memory

Places I Visited On The Park

Next Time I will

Notes

Will Return once again?

Yep / Nope

Overall Experience

ARCHES

City/State Entered	Temp

  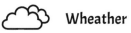 **Wheather**

Who Was With Me	Where We Stayed	Activities We Did

Wildlife	Sights

Impressions

My Favorite Memory

Places I Visited On The Park

Next Time I will

Notes

Will Return once again?

Yep / Nope

Overall Experience

BADLANDS

City/State Entered	Temp

  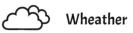 Wheather

Who Was With Me	Where We Stayed	Activities We Did

Wildlife	Sights

Impressions

My Favorite Memory

Places I Visited On The Park

Next Time I will

Notes

Will Return once again?

Yep / Nope

Overall Experience

BIG BEND

City/State Entered	Temp

  Wheather

Who Was With Me	Where We Stayed	Activities We Did

Wildlife	Sights

Impressions

My Favorite Memory

Places I Visited On The Park

Next Time I will

Notes

Will Return once again?

Yep / Nope

Overall Experience

BISCAYNE

City/State Entered	Temp

 Wheather

Who Was With Me	Where We Stayed	Activities We Did

Wildlife	Sights

Impressions

My Favorite Memory

Places I Visited On The Park

Next Time I will

Notes

Will Return once again?

Yep / Nope

Overall Experience

☆☆☆☆☆

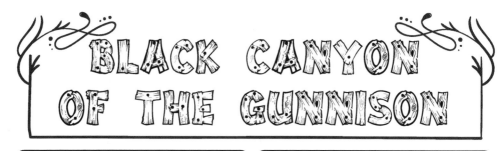

BLACK CANYON OF THE GUNNISON

City/State Entered	Temp

 Wheather

Who Was With Me

Where We Stayed

Activities We Did

Wildlife

Sights

Impressions

My Favorite Memory

Places I Visited On The Park

Next Time I will

Notes

Will Return once again?

Yep / Nope

Overall Experience

BRYCE CANYON

City/State Entered	Temp

  Wheather

Who Was With Me	Where We Stayed	Activities We Did

Wildlife	Sights

Impressions

My Favorite Memory

Places I Visited On The Park

Next Time I will

Notes

Will Return once again?

Yep / Nope

Overall Experience

CANYONLANDS

City/State Entered	Temp

   Wheather

Who Was With Me	Where We Stayed	Activities We Did

Wildlife

Sights

Impressions

My Favorite Memory

Places I Visited On The Park

Next Time I will

Notes

Will Return once again?

Yep / Nope

Overall Experience

CAPITOL REEF

City/State Entered	Temp

   Wheather

Who Was With Me	Where We Stayed	Activities We Did

Wildlife	Sights

Impressions

My Favorite Memory

Places I Visited On The Park

Next Time I will

Notes

Will Return once again?

Yep / Nope

Overall Experience

CARLSBAD CAVERNS

City/State Entered	Temp

  Wheather

Who Was With Me	Where We Stayed	Activities We Did

Wildlife	Sights

Impressions

My Favorite Memory

Places I Visited On The Park

Next Time I will

Notes

Will Return once again?

Yep / Nope

Overall Experience

CHANNEL ISLANDS

City/State Entered	Temp

   Wheather

Who Was With Me	Where We Stayed	Activities We Did

Wildlife	Sights

Impressions

My Favorite Memory

Places I Visited On The Park

Next Time I will

Notes

Will Return once again?

Yep / Nope

Overall Experience

CONGAREE

City/State Entered	Temp

   Wheather

Who Was With Me	Where We Stayed	Activities We Did

Wildlife	Sights

Impressions

My Favorite Memory

Places I Visited On The Park

Next Time I will

Notes

Will Return once again?

Yep / Nope

Overall Experience

CRATER LAKE

City/State Entered	Temp

   Wheather

Who Was With Me	Where We Stayed	Activities We Did

Wildlife	Sights

Impressions

My Favorite Memory

Places I Visited On The Park

Next Time I will

Notes

Will Return once again?

Yep / Nope

Overall Experience

CUYAHOGA VALLEY

City/State Entered	Temp

  Wheather

Who Was With Me	Where We Stayed	Activities We Did

Wildlife	Sights

Impressions

My Favorite Memory

Places I Visited On The Park

Next Time I will

Notes

Will Return once again?

Yep / Nope

Overall Experience

☆ ☆ ☆ ☆ ☆

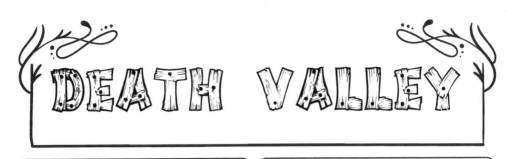

DEATH VALLEY

City/State Entered	Temp

   Wheather

Who Was With Me	Where We Stayed	Activities We Did

Wildlife	Sights

Impressions

My Favorite Memory

Places I Visited On The Park

Next Time I will

Notes

Will Return once again?	Overall Experience
Yep / Nope	

DENALI

City/State Entered	Temp

   Wheather

Who Was With Me	Where We Stayed	Activities We Did

Wildlife	Sights

Impressions

My Favorite Memory

Places I Visited On The Park

Next Time I will

Notes

Will Return once again?

Yep / Nope

Overall Experience

DRY TORTUGAS

City/State Entered	Temp

   Wheather

Who Was With Me	Where We Stayed	Activities We Did

Wildlife	Sights

Impressions

My Favorite Memory

Places I Visited On The Park

Next Time I will

Notes

Will Return once again?

Yep / Nope

Overall Experience

EVERGLADES

City/State Entered	Temp

   Wheather

Who Was With Me	Where We Stayed	Activities We Did

Wildlife	Sights

Impressions

My Favorite Memory

Places I Visited On The Park

Next Time I will

Notes

Will Return once again?

Yep / Nope

Overall Experience

GATES OF THE ARCTIC

City/State Entered	Temp

  Wheather

Who Was With Me	Where We Stayed	Activities We Did

Wildlife	Sights

Impressions

My Favorite Memory

Places I Visited On The Park

Next Time I will

Notes

Will Return once again?

Yep / Nope

Overall Experience

☆☆☆☆☆

GLACIER BAY

City/State Entered	Temp

   Wheather

Who Was With Me	Where We Stayed	Activities We Did

Wildlife	Sights

Impressions

My Favorite Memory

Places I Visited On The Park

Next Time I will

Notes

Will Return once again?

Yep / Nope

Overall Experience

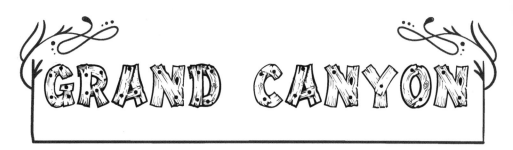

GRAND CANYON

City/State Entered	Temp

  Wheather

Who Was With Me	Where We Stayed	Activities We Did

Wildlife	Sights

Impressions

My Favorite Memory

Places I Visited On The Park

Next Time I will

Notes

Will Return once again?

Yep / Nope

Overall Experience

GRAND TETON

City/State Entered	Temp

  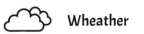 Wheather

Who Was With Me	Where We Stayed	Activities We Did

Wildlife	Sights

Impressions

My Favorite Memory

Places I Visited On The Park

Next Time I will

Notes

Will Return once again?

Yep / Nope

Overall Experience

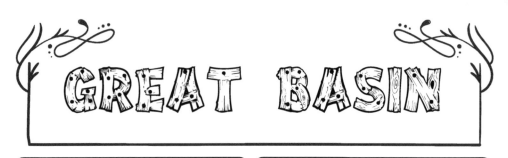

GREAT BASIN

City/State Entered	Temp

 Wheather

Who Was With Me	Where We Stayed	Activities We Did

Wildlife	Sights

Impressions

My Favorite Memory

Places I Visited On The Park

Next Time I will

Notes

Will Return once again?

Yep / Nope

Overall Experience

GREAT SAND DUNES

City/State Entered	Temp

  Wheather

Who Was With Me	Where We Stayed	Activities We Did

Wildlife	Sights

Impressions

My Favorite Memory

Places I Visited On The Park

Next Time I will

Notes

Will Return once again?

Yep / Nope

Overall Experience

GREAT SMOKY MOUNTAINS

City/State Entered	Temp

Wheather

Who Was With Me	Where We Stayed	Activities We Did

Wildlife	Sights

Impressions

My Favorite Memory

Places I Visited On The Park

Next Time I will

Notes

Will Return once again?

Yep / Nope

Overall Experience

GUADALUPE MOUNTAINS

City/State Entered	Temp

  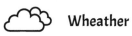 Wheather

Who Was With Me	Where We Stayed	Activities We Did

Wildlife	Sights

Impressions

My Favorite Memory

Places I Visited On The Park

Next Time I will

Notes

Will Return once again?

Yep / Nope

Overall Experience

HALEAKAL

City/State Entered	Temp

 Wheather

Who Was With Me	Where We Stayed	Activities We Did

Wildlife	Sights

Impressions

My Favorite Memory

Places I Visited On The Park

Next Time I will

Notes

Will Return once again?

Yep / Nope

Overall Experience

HAWAII VOLCANOES

City/State Entered	Temp

  Wheather

Who Was With Me	Where We Stayed	Activities We Did

Wildlife

Sights

Impressions

My Favorite Memory

Places I Visited On The Park

Next Time I will

Notes

Will Return once again?

Yep / Nope

Overall Experience

HOT SPRINGS

City/State Entered	Temp

 Wheather

Who Was With Me	Where We Stayed	Activities We Did

Wildlife	Sights

Impressions

My Favorite Memory

Places I Visited On The Park

Next Time I will

Notes

Will Return once again?

Yep / Nope

Overall Experience

INDIANA DUNES

City/State Entered	Temp

Wheather

Who Was With Me	Where We Stayed	Activities We Did

Wildlife	Sights

Impressions

My Favorite Memory

Places I Visited On The Park

Next Time I will

Notes

Will Return once again?

Yep / Nope

Overall Experience

ISLE ROYALE

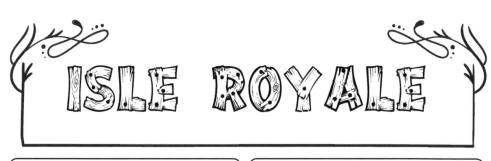

City/State Entered	Temp

 Wheather

Who Was With Me	Where We Stayed	Activities We Did

Wildlife	Sights

Impressions

My Favorite Memory

Places I Visited On The Park

Next Time I will

Notes

Will Return once again?

Yep / Nope

Overall Experience

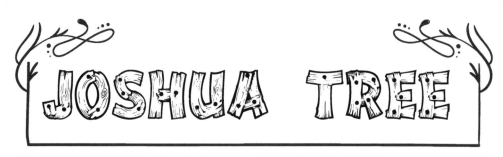

JOSHUA TREE

City/State Entered	Temp

  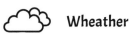 Wheather

Who Was With Me	Where We Stayed	Activities We Did

Wildlife	Sights

Impressions

My Favorite Memory

Places I Visited On The Park

Next Time I will

Notes

Will Return once again?

Yep / Nope

Overall Experience

KATMAI

City/State Entered

Temp

  Wheather

Who Was With Me

Where We Stayed

Activities We Did

Wildlife

Sights

Impressions

My Favorite Memory

Places I Visited On The Park

Next Time I will

Notes

Will Return once again?

Yep / Nope

Overall Experience

KENAI FJORDS

City/State Entered	Temp

  Wheather

Who Was With Me	Where We Stayed	Activities We Did

Wildlife	Sights

Impressions

My Favorite Memory

Places I Visited On The Park

Next Time I will

Notes

Will Return once again?

Yep / Nope

Overall Experience

KINGS CANYON

City/State Entered	Temp

Wheather

Who Was With Me	Where We Stayed	Activities We Did

Wildlife	Sights

Impressions

My Favorite Memory

Places I Visited On The Park

Next Time I will

Notes

Will Return once again?

Yep / Nope

Overall Experience

KOBUK VALLEY

City/State Entered	Temp

 Wheather

Who Was With Me	Where We Stayed	Activities We Did

Wildlife	Sights

Impressions

My Favorite Memory

Places I Visited On The Park

Next Time I will

Notes

Will Return once again?

Yep / Nope

Overall Experience

LAKE CLARK

City/State Entered	Temp

   Wheather

Who Was With Me	Where We Stayed	Activities We Did

Wildlife	Sights

Impressions

My Favorite Memory

Places I Visited On The Park

Next Time I will

Notes

Will Return once again?

Yep / Nope

Overall Experience

LASSEN VOLCANIC

City/State Entered	Temp

Wheather

Who Was With Me	Where We Stayed	Activities We Did

Wildlife	Sights

Impressions

My Favorite Memory

Places I Visited On The Park

Next Time I will

Notes

Will Return once again?

Yep / Nope

Overall Experience

MAMMOTH CAVE

City/State Entered	Temp

 Wheather

Who Was With Me	Where We Stayed	Activities We Did

Wildlife	Sights

Impressions

My Favorite Memory

Places I Visited On The Park

Next Time I will

Notes

Will Return once again?

Yep / Nope

Overall Experience

MESA VERDE

City/State Entered	Temp

Wheather

Who Was With Me	Where We Stayed	Activities We Did

Wildlife	Sights

Impressions

My Favorite Memory

Places I Visited On The Park

Next Time I will

Notes

Will Return once again?

Yep / Nope

Overall Experience

MOUNT RAINIER

City/State Entered

 Temp

  Wheather

Who Was With Me	Where We Stayed	Activities We Did

Wildlife

Sights

Impressions

My Favorite Memory

Places I Visited On The Park

Next Time I will

Notes

Will Return once again?

Yep / Nope

Overall Experience

NEW RIVER GORGE

City/State Entered	Temp

   Wheather

Who Was With Me	Where We Stayed	Activities We Did

Wildlife	Sights

Impressions

My Favorite Memory

Places I Visited On The Park

Next Time I will

Notes

Will Return once again?

Yep / Nope

Overall Experience

NORTH CASCADES

City/State Entered	Temp

   Wheather

Who Was With Me	Where We Stayed	Activities We Did

Wildlife	Sights

Impressions

My Favorite Memory

Places I Visited On The Park

Next Time I will

Notes

Will Return once again?

Yep / Nope

Overall Experience

PETRIFIED FOREST

City/State Entered	Temp

  Wheather

Who Was With Me	Where We Stayed	Activities We Did

Wildlife	Sights

Impressions

My Favorite Memory

Places I Visited On The Park

Next Time I will

Notes

Will Return once again?

Yep / Nope

Overall Experience

PINNACLES

City/State Entered	Temp

  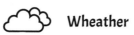 Wheather

Who Was With Me	Where We Stayed	Activities We Did

Wildlife	Sights

Impressions

My Favorite Memory

Places I Visited On The Park

Next Time I will

Notes

Will Return once again?

Yep / Nope

Overall Experience

REDWOOD

City/State Entered	Temp

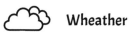 Wheather

Who Was With Me	Where We Stayed	Activities We Did

Wildlife	Sights

Impressions

My Favorite Memory

Places I Visited On The Park

Next Time I will

Notes

Will Return once again?

Yep / Nope

Overall Experience

ROCKY MOUNTAIN

City/State Entered

Temp

  Wheather

Who Was With Me

Where We Stayed

Activities We Did

Wildlife

Sights

Impressions

My Favorite Memory

Places I Visited On The Park

Next Time I will

Notes

Will Return once again?

Yep / Nope

Overall Experience

SAGUARO

City/State Entered	Temp

   Wheather

Who Was With Me	Where We Stayed	Activities We Did

Wildlife	Sights

Impressions

My Favorite Memory

Places I Visited On The Park

Next Time I will

Notes

Will Return once again?

Yep / Nope

Overall Experience

SHENANDOAH

City/State Entered	Temp

  Wheather

Who Was With Me	Where We Stayed	Activities We Did

Wildlife	Sights

Impressions

My Favorite Memory

Places I Visited On The Park

Next Time I will

Notes

Will Return once again?

Yep / Nope

Overall Experience

THEODORE ROOSEVELT

City/State Entered	Temp

   Wheather

Who Was With Me	Where We Stayed	Activities We Did

Wildlife	Sights

Impressions

My Favorite Memory

Places I Visited On The Park

Next Time I will

Notes

Will Return once again?

Yep / Nope

Overall Experience

VIRGIN ISLANDS

City/State Entered	Temp

 Wheather

Who Was With Me	Where We Stayed	Activities We Did

Wildlife	Sights

Impressions

My Favorite Memory

Places I Visited On The Park

Next Time I will

Notes

Will Return once again?

Yep / Nope

Overall Experience

VOYAGEURS

City/State Entered	Temp

  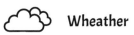 Wheather

Who Was With Me	Where We Stayed	Activities We Did

Wildlife	Sights

Impressions

My Favorite Memory

Places I Visited On The Park

Next Time I will

Notes

Will Return once again?

Yep / Nope

Overall Experience

WHITE SANDS

City/State Entered	Temp

   Wheather

Who Was With Me

Where We Stayed

Activities We Did

Wildlife

Sights

Impressions

My Favorite Memory

Places I Visited On The Park

Next Time I will

Notes

Will Return once again?

Yep / Nope

Overall Experience

WIND CAVE

City/State Entered

Temp

Wheather

Who Was With Me

Where We Stayed

Activities We Did

Wildlife

Sights

Impressions

My Favorite Memory

Places I Visited On The Park

Next Time I will

Notes

Will Return once again?

Yep / Nope

Overall Experience

WRANGELL ST. ELIAS

City/State Entered

Temp

  **Wheather**

Who Was With Me

Where We Stayed

Activities We Did

Wildlife

Sights

Impressions

My Favorite Memory

Places I Visited On The Park

Next Time I will

Notes

Will Return once again?

Yep / Nope

Overall Experience

YELLOWSTONE

City/State Entered	Temp

  **Wheather**

Who Was With Me	Where We Stayed	Activities We Did

Wildlife	Sights

Impressions

My Favorite Memory

Places I Visited On The Park

Next Time I will

Notes

Will Return once again?

Yep / Nope

Overall Experience

YOSEMITE

City/State Entered	Temp

   Wheather

Who Was With Me	Where We Stayed	Activities We Did

Wildlife

Sights

Impressions

My Favorite Memory

Places I Visited On The Park

Next Time I will

Notes

Will Return once again?

Yep / Nope

Overall Experience

ZION

City/State Entered	Temp

   Wheather

Who Was With Me	Where We Stayed	Activities We Did

Wildlife	Sights

Impressions